Student Assessment Book

Developmental Reading Assessment®

Word Analysis

by Joetta M. Beaver
In Collaboration With Reading/Classroom Teachers

PEARSON

Pearson® is a trademark, in the U.S. and/or in other countries, of Pearson plc, or its affiliates.

Developmental Reading Assessment® and Celebration Press® are registered trademarks and the DRA™ logo is a trademark, in the U.S. and/or in other countries, of Pearson plc, or its affiliates.

ISBN 13:   978-0-7652-3328-8
ISBN 10:   0-7652-3328-2

Printed in the United States of America

17 V059 12 11 10

Distinguishing pictured rhyming words

Distinguishing pictured rhyming words

Distinguishing initial sounds of pictured words

6   Distinguishing initial sounds of pictured words

O	A	X	B
S	C	E	T
K	P	I	D
M	L	R	Z
N	F	W	H
U	G	Y	Q
J	V		

Recognizing capital letters

o   x   s   c

e   k   r   z

m   a   w   p

t   n   y   f

h   g   v   l

u   q   i   b

j   d

Recognizing lowercase letters

My cat is black.

My cat is on the mat.

My cat is playing now.

1	2	3	4	5	6

Segmenting sentences into words

I	in	is	look
the	dog	you	my
a	to	can	at
go	see	he	on
up	and	it	like

t

s	f	n	a	b
p	z	c	o	y
t	r	h	d	e
m	j	l	g	u
k	v	w	i	

Identifying and using initial sounds

big	will	but	help	did
one	are	all	old	had
play	for	said	get	they
stop	little	eat	his	ask
do	not	home	was	time
she	by	out	have	him

1.

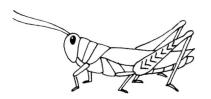

2.

3.

4.

5.

6.

7.

8.

Segmenting words into syllables I

_____

first	went	next	boy	place
down	door	some	make	great
under	because	then	tell	move
run	right	girl	more	just
each	again	about	of	from
this	made	with	when	back
only	year	tree	animal	off
your	try	man	saw	over
before	around	that	find	as
them	walk	good	most	call

☆

> like
>
> bike
>
> hike

1.

> will
>
> hill
>
> still

2.

> can
>
> fan
>
> plan

3.

> then
>
> when
>
> men

4.

> my
>
> why
>
> try

5.

> mat
>
> that
>
> flat

6.

> stop
>
> drop
>
> plop

7.

> know
>
> snow
>
> slow

8.

> gold
>
> told
>
> cold

9.

> right
>
> night
>
> bright

Substituting onsets: rhyming words

☆

big
bit
bid

1.

will
win
with

2.

him
his
hid

3.

bus
bug
bump

4.

dog
doll
dot

5.

must
mug
much

6.

had
has
hand

7.

can
camp
cab

8.

home
hope
hose

9.

cake
came
cape

Substituting final sounds

☆ gr

1.	st	7.	sn
2.	pl	8.	sw
3.	tr	9.	sp
4.	dr	10.	gl
5.	bl	11.	sm
6.	fr	12.	str

Blending and using initial consonant sounds

1.

lot
know
boat
hope

2.

take
way
rain
mad

3.

bed
feel
beat
Pete

4.

night
kit
tie
wise

5.

bug
fruit
true
cube

Identifying words with long and short vowels

☆ jumped

_____

1. himself

2. broken

3. deeper

4. couldn't

5. longest

6. she'll

7. landed

8. cloudy

people	would	feet	after	way
children	away	much	felt	head
any	behind	what	here	were
came	put	live	water	hard
could	house	must	take	thought
boat	their	now	work	there
even	need	long	want	shout
very	other	think	her	watch
thing	know	who	last	began
been	picture	start	better	well

1.

ship

sharp

shell

shore

sheet

shoot

2.

plum

place

plant

plate

please

plead

3.

truck

train

trim

treat

track

trot

4.

stay

stamp

steep

stair

stem

stir

5.

grow

grape

ground

grill

grab

grew

6.

bright

brush

brand

brought

brain

broil

1. knight   5. spray

2. stream   6. crew

3. clever   7. thread

4. frown   8. quite

☆
tree	
trade	
made	

1.
know	
knight	
right	

2.
street	
stream	
team	

3.
class	
clever	
never	

4.
from	
frown	
down	

5.
spring	
spray	
day	

6.
cry	
crew	
new	

7.
three	
thread	
head	

8.
queen	
quite	
kite	

1.

bloom

loose

smooth

balloon

raccoon

2.

freedom

speech

needle

fifteen

agree

3.

march

artist

garden

alarm

argue

4.

explain

afraid

paint

trail

straight

5.

soap

throat

toaster

coach

charcoal

6.

flight

lightning

frighten

highest

sigh

☆   rac

_____

1.   prob

2.   min

3.   prin

4.   rab

5.   soc

6.   cam

7.   bro

8.   oc

9.   thun

10.   bas

☆   running

☆   blackberry

---

1.   kitten

2.   raincoat

3.   table

4.   butterfly

5.   backpacking

6.   firmly

7.   newspaper

8.   babies

9.   reminded

☆   reporter

_____

1. helpless

2. dangerous

3. magical

4. respectful

5. duckling

6. darkness

7. finally

8. motorcyclist

☆   disobey

_____

1. impossible

2. disappear

3. preschool

4. submarine

5. tricycle

6. recapture

7. endanger

8. uncertain

☆　finalist

_____

1.　decision

2.　imaginary

3.　attendance

4.　suddenly

5.　sinkable

6.　photographer

7.　explanation

8.　especially

☆ different

☆ tomorrow

1. apartment

2. adventure

3. terrible

4. generous

5. enough

6. uninviting

7. information

8. suddenly

9. insisted